Enjoying the Library

the

Book C

Written by Jane Price

Published by Prim-Ed Publishing

Enjoying the Library

A Library Skills Programme for Primary Schools
Book C

The *Enjoying The Library* series comprises six sequential packages, catering for all Year levels in the primary school. The packages are self-explanatory and have been designed for use in any library, regardless of the number of resources available to the pupils.

It should be stressed that the activities in the series are designed to be used by both classroom teachers and library specialists.

The series involves a thorough library programme. The emphasis is on 'hands-on' experience as this not only caters for individual abilities and differences but also gives pupils the opportunity to explore the resources available in the library.

The aim of this programme is to make students independent library users who can choose and use appropriate, relevant library resources. Specific reference to many parts of the shelves has been made to enable pupils to become familiar with the wide range of subjects offered.

Each package contains some forty activities lasting approximately thirty minutes each. This provides a complete year-long library study programme. However, in many schools a second period per week is also given. It is important that in the second session all pupils are given the opportunity to borrow resources. Lower primary pupils enjoy this time to be read a range of stories or be given the opportunity to complete any library work.

Suggestions for further research are given in the packages for the middle and upper primary Year levels. Appropriately, a research question relating to specific classroom activities should be given.

Caring for Books

Library books are precious as not only are they enjoyable resources, but they cost money and other people will also want to read them.

Below are a few simple suggestions to make sure books are cared for.

1. **Use a library bag.**

2. **Keep your books out of the sun and damp places.**

3. **No tearing, scribbling or spilling food onto your books.**

4. **Always put your books in a safe place where you can find them.**

5. **Always have clean hands before you begin to read.**

Revision

How do you borrow a book?

_____

_____

_____

_____

Who works in the library?

_____

_____

To where do you return
your books?

_____

How many books can you
borrow at one time?

_____

For how long can you borrow
a book?

_____

Discuss this with your teacher.

Library Plan

Cut out the following sections of a library and paste them on a blank piece of paper to arrange your own library floor plan.

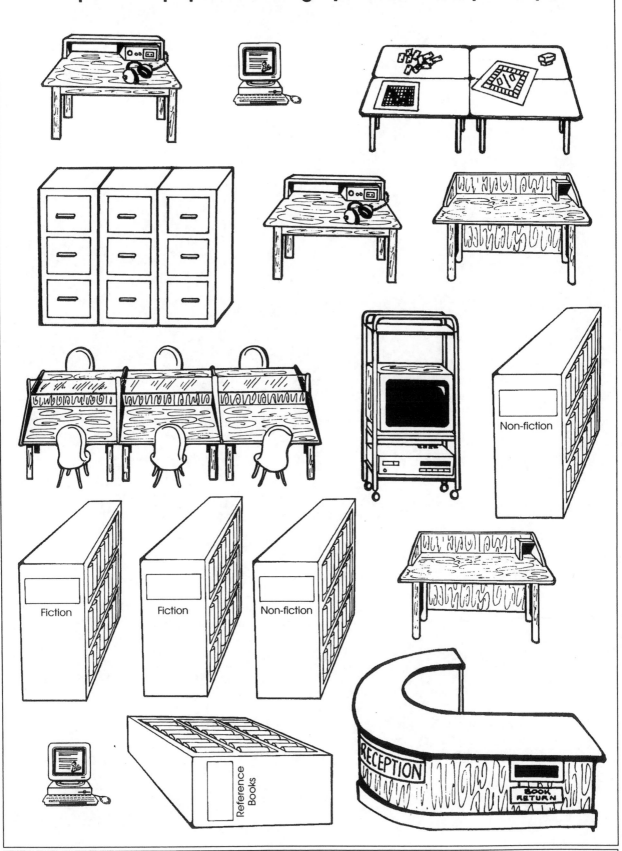

Areas in the Library

From your plan, list the three main areas you drew.

* F _____

* N _____

* R _____

Think of as many examples of each of these as you can.

F_____	N_____	R_____
Examples:	Examples:	Examples:
_____	_____	_____
_____	_____	_____
_____	_____	_____
_____	_____	_____
_____	_____	_____
_____	_____	_____

Are you able to borrrow books from these three areas?

Fiction _____

Non-fiction _____

Reference _____

Fiction

What is fiction?_____

_____

How are the fiction books arranged on the shelves?_____

_____

Put these authors' surnames in alphabetical order.

Pilling   Sharp   Robinson   Norman

Dahl   Arrick   Mahy

Kennedy   Watson   Smith

1. _____   6. _____

2. _____   7. _____

3. _____   8. _____

4. _____   9. _____

5. _____   10. _____

What is a title?_____

_____

What is an author?_____

_____

Write down the author, title and spine label of the above book.

    Author:_____

    Title:_____

    Spine label:_____

Write the author, title and spine label of a book from the fiction shelf.

    Author:_____

    Title:_____

    Spine label:_____

Using the Catalogue - Fiction

Choose a book and fill in the details on the card below.

Call number: _____

Title:

Illustrator:

*Publishing data:

_____

_____

_____

_____

_____

○

Author:

Collation (no. of pages)

```
636.08
The Wideawake Mice
McCullagh, Sheila
Illus. by Prue Theobalds
Ladybird Books,
Loughborough
88p. Illus. 23cm
                    ○
```

* Teacher to complete

Using the catalogue, complete the following:

* A. Find the author of these titles:

   1. _____

   2. _____

   3. _____

   4. _____

   5. _____

* B. Find the title of a book written by these authors:

   1. _____

   2. _____

   3. _____

   4. _____

   5. _____

FICTION BOOK

Using the Computer - Fiction

Fill in the computer screen below.

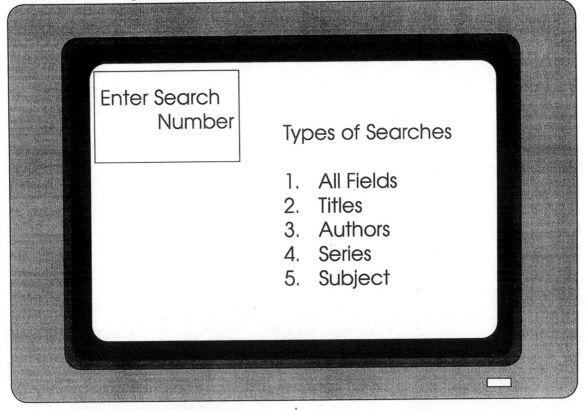

Enter Search
Number

Types of Searches

1. All Fields
2. Titles
3. Authors
4. Series
5. Subject

Which search would you do if you only knew one word in the title of a fiction book you would like to find?

_____

Which search would you do if you knew the title of the fiction book you were looking for?

_____

Which search would you do if you only knew the author of the fiction book you were looking for?

_____

Using the computer, find out whether your library has:

Books with the following titles:
- *Esio Trot*
- *Unbelievable*
- *Anastasia*
- *Way Home*

Books by the following authors:
- Jennings, Paul
- Blume, Judy
- Klein, Robin
- Dahl, Roald

Fiction - Picture Books

Your teacher will give you a picture book for this activity.

Title:_____

Author:_____

What things make picture books special?

_____

_____

_____

_____

Read the picture book you have been given.

Did you enjoy it? Why/Why not?

_____

_____

_____

Draw a character from the picture book you have just read.

Fiction Test

1. What is fiction?_____

   _____

2. How are fiction books arranged on the shelves?_____

   _____

3. **Write these authors' surnames in alphabetical order.**

   Briggs   Zindel   Seuss   Mahy   Blyton   Martin

   1._____   2._____   3._____

   4._____   5._____   6._____

4. **Choose a book from the fiction shelf.**

   Write down the:

   Author: _____

   Title: _____

5.

   TIKA, THE DANCING ELEPHANT

   BY BART SHEEZEVY

Fiction Sleuth

R	E	A	F	S	K	O	O	B	E	R	U	T	C	I	P	D
I	C	K	L	E	I	N	T	B	C	O	M	P	U	T	E	R
N	O	G	E	M	I	S	I	R	G	R	E	P	A	G	E	S
A	L	P	H	A	B	E	T	I	C	A	L	O	R	D	E	R
U	L	U	S	H	A	T	L	G	F	U	N	Y	O	U	M	C
T	L	B	A	Y	N	R	E	G	E	A	D	A	N	Y	A	W
H	A	L	H	E	S	E	U	S	S	S	H	A	R	P	N	R
O	T	I	B	R	H	Y	M	E	E	L	I	B	R	A	R	Y
R	I	S	L	A	S	E	C	N	E	R	E	F	E	R	U	N
A	O	H	U	S	L	E	B	A	L	E	N	I	P	S	S	D
T	N	E	M	A	T	A	N	N	A	I	R	A	R	B	I	L
A	Y	R	E	T	I	N	U	M	E	R	I	C	A	L	M	E
D	F	I	C	T	I	O	N	E	U	G	O	L	A	T	A	C

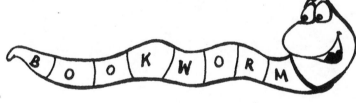

Find the following words.

Alphabetical Order
Author
Blume
Briggs
Catalogue
Collation
Computer
Data

Fiction
Klein
Librarian
Library
Mahy
Numerical
Pages
Picture Books

Publisher
References
Rhyme
Seuss
Sharp
Shelf
Spine Labels
Surname
Title

There is a message left. Can you find it?

_____

_____

Non-fiction

What are non-fiction books?

_____

_____

How are they arranged on the non-fiction shelves?

_____

_____

_____

Put these numbers into order from smallest to largest.

821	623	100	909	500
001	245	323	450	746

____ ____ ____ ____ ____

____ ____ ____ ____ ____

The number on a non-fiction book relates to a subject.
Go to the numbers below and write down the subject you
find. For example 636.7 - Dogs.

004 _____   796.323 _____

567.91 _____   952 _____

595.4 _____

Parts of a Non-fiction Book

Title ———— Poetry for Children

By
S. Miling

Author ————

Spine Label ———— 821 MIL

What is this book about?_____

Choose a non-fiction book from the shelf.

Write down the:

    (a) Author:_____

    (b) Title:_____

    (c) Subject:_____

    (d) Spine label:_____

What do you think of the book you chose?_____

_____

_____

Fill in the missing details on the catalogue card/computer screen.

C _____

N _____

Title: _____

I _____

Collation
(no. of
pages)

A _____

Publisher

636.08
McCullagh, Sheila
The Wideawake Mice
Illus. by P. Theobalds
Ladybird Books Ltd,
Loughborough
Leicestershire, England
45p. Illus. 45
Puddle Lane Books
○

Title

636.08

The Wideawake Mice

McCullagh,Sheila

Illus. by P. Theobalds

Ladybird Books Ltd,
Loughborough

45p. Illus. 45
○

Author

636.08

McCullagh, Sheila

The Wideawake Mice

Illus. by P. Theobalds

Ladybird Books Ltd,
Loughborough

45p. Illus. 45

Puddle Lane Books
○

Subject

636.08

The Wideawake Mice

McCullagh, Sheila

Illus. by P. Theobalds

Ladybird Books Ltd,
Loughborough

Puddle Lane Books
○

Complete the following sentences.

A. You can't remember the author of the book *Computers*. You

would look up the _____ in the catalogue/computer.

B. You want to find a book by Lambert. You would look

up_____ in the catalogue/computer.

C. You need information on the grooming and care of dogs for a

project. You would look up _____ in the catalogue/

computer.

Non-fiction Shelves

The non-fiction shelves are arranged numerically from 000 - 999.

Write down the subjects covered under each of these numbers. (Look at the signs — your teacher will help you.)

000 _____

100 _____

200 _____

300 _____

400 _____

500 ___*Science*_____

600 _____

700 ___*Theatre, Sport*_____

800 _____

900 _____

Choose one non-fiction book. Write down the following:

Spine Label: [ ]

Author: _____

Title: _____

Subject: _____

Using an Index

Most non-fiction books have an index at the back of the book.

An index is an alphabetical listing of the subjects in the book.

Example:

INDEX

Apple 1 - 3	Fruit 1 - 16
Apricot 4	Grapes 15
Avocado 6	Lemon 13 - 14
Banana 5	Mandarine 7
Beetroot 22	Orange 8 - 9
Cabbage 18	Pepper 23
Carrot 21	Radish 20
Cauliflower 19	Vegetables 17 - 25
Damson 17	

Answer these questions using the above index.

1. How many pages discuss vegetables?_____

2. How many pages discuss fruit?_____

3. What page do we find these subjects on:

Lemon?_____   Radish?_____

Apple?_____   Vegetable?_____

Grape?_____   Banana?_____

Beetroot?_____   Pepper?_____

Cauliflower?_____   Apricot?_____

Locating Non-fiction Resources

Non-fiction books are arranged by numbers according to their subject. A man called Melvil Dewey arranged the subjects into groups of numbers to make it easier for us to find the books we want.

How are the shelves arranged?_____

_____

_____

Between which two numbers on the shelves would you find these books?

000-100	100-200	200-300	300-400	400-500	500-600	600-700	700-800	800-900	900-999

Science 505_____   Computers 001.64_____

Sport 796_____   Geography 900s_____

Poetry 821_____   Navy 359_____

THE NAVY

Using the Subject Heading Index

How do you use an index? _____

_____

_____

_____

Look through the subject heading index.

How is it arranged?_____

_____

_____

_____

_____

Can you find the following subjects?

What number are they found at?

Football_____ Computers_____

Cats_____ Japan_____

Gymnastics_____ Japanese Cooking_____

How many did you find?_____

Doing a
Subject Search

What number search is a subject search?

_____

What other search can we do that will also locate subjects?

_____

Using the subject search, what are the numbers of the following subjects?

Football_____   Computers_____

Cats_____   Japan_____

Gymnastics_____   Japanese Cooking_____

How many items does your library have in relation to these subjects?

Football_____   Computer_____

Cats_____   Japan_____

Gymnastics_____   Japanese Cooking_____

Subject Searches 1

How are the non-fiction books arranged?

_____

Give the Dewey number for the following subjects:

Ships_____   Origami_____

Clowns_____   Farmers _____

Gold_____   Amphibians_____

Piano_____   Rice_____

Penguin_____   Honey_____

Choose any subject starting with P _____

Locate the Dewey number. _____

Write some notes on the subject. _____

_____

_____

_____

_____

_____

_____

Subject Searches 2

The yellow subject heading index gives you the numbers of the subject you are looking for.

Find the numbers for these subjects:

Pottery_____

Horse Riding _____

Hockey_____

Ships_____

Health _____

Fungi_____

Kangaroos_____

Football_____

Copper_____

Beetles_____

Locate one of these numbers on the shelf and choose a book.

Author:_____

Title:_____

What did you think of the book?_____

_____

_____

Subject Searches 3

What subjects have these numbers? You will need to use the front of the index to complete this.

370_____ 400_____

160_____ 570_____

510_____ 700_____

780_____ 220_____

340_____ 690_____

What are the numbers for the following subjects?

Medicine_____ Numbers_____

Noise_____ Medals_____

Scorpions_____ Incas _____

Water Sports _____ Wasps_____

Did you find this easy?_____

Put these spine labels into numerical order, as if you were putting them back on the shelf.

001.5	765	035.2
BRA	TRE	CAN

994.94	567.5	796.7
SIX	SCI	SPO

1._____ 4._____

2._____ 5._____

3._____ 6._____

Subject Searches 4

1. Write down one of your hobbies. _____

_____

2. What is the Dewey number for your hobby? _____

3. Using the subheadings below as a guide, tell about your hobby.

   * Equipment

   * Rules, methods etc.

   * Instructions

   * Draw a picture to help describe your hobby.

_____

_____

_____

_____

_____

_____

_____

_____

_____

_____

Using Non-fiction
Information 1

Roses

Roses are beautiful flowers. They grow from small plants into lovely bushes. You plant them in springtime, water them often and look after them. Follow these simple steps and you will have lots of beautiful roses.

Watch out for the sharp thorns. They protect the rose from harm.

Roses are sweetly scented. They are often made into perfume.

Answer these questions.

1. When should you plant a rosebush?_____

   _____

2. How do you care for rosebushes?_____

   _____

3. What helps protect the roses?_____

   _____

4. What can be made from rose

   petals?_____

   _____

5. Draw a beautiful rose.

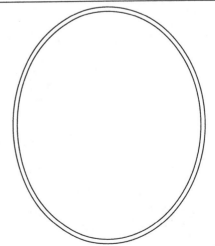

Using Non-fiction
Information 2

Hail

Small lumps of ice that fall from thunderclouds are known as hail. Hail is usually round and no larger than a pebble. The largest known hailstone is said to have been as big as a person's head.

Hail forms when water droplets freeze inside thunderclouds. Hailstones gain several layers of ice, growing larger. Hail falls in short, sharp showers known as hailstorms. Although hail only falls in small amounts, hailstorms can cause a lot of damage to fields and crops, as well as break glass windows.

Answer the following questions:

1. What is hail?_____

2. What was the size of the largest hailstone known?_____

    _____

3. How do hailstones form?_____

    _____

4. What damage can occur during a hailstorm?_____

    _____

5. What is the Dewey number for Weather?_____

6. Locate one non-fiction book which contains some information on hail. Write down the:

    Author:_____

    Title:_____

    Page number of information on hail:_____

Using Pictures for Information

Your teacher will show you a chart.

Write down some notes about the chart.

_____   _____

_____   _____

_____   _____

_____

_____

Write a few sentences telling about the chart.

_____

_____

_____

_____

_____

_____

_____

_____

_____

Explosion Chart

Choose one of the following topics.

Space

Travel   Ballet

Sport   Trucks

Animals

Write as many things about the topic as you can think of.
For example; rules, homes, uniform.

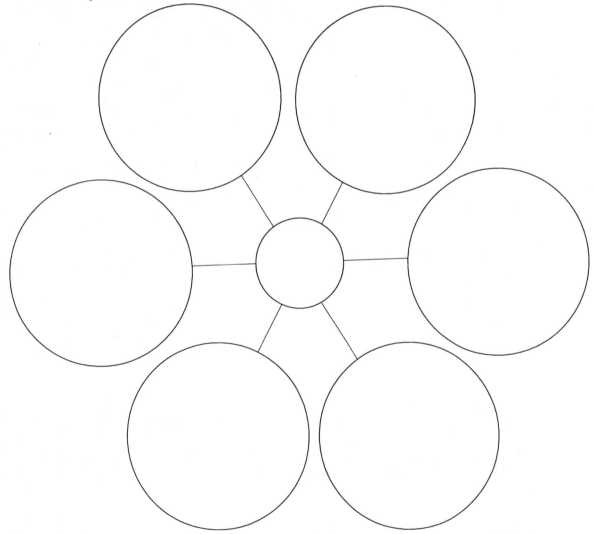

What do you need to find out about the topic you chose?

_____

_____

Audiovisual Material

Audiovisual means both hearing and seeing.

Draw a picture next to each of the words below.

Video Cassette	Audio Cassette Recorder

Video Cassette Recorder	Cassette

Chart/Poster	Listen to a story on a tape while working through this sheet.

Folktales and Fables

Listen to a folktale or fable.

Draw what the story was about. Make sure you draw the pictures in the correct order.

1.	2.
3.	4.
5.	6.

Fairytales

Listen to a fairytale.

Design a new cover for the book.

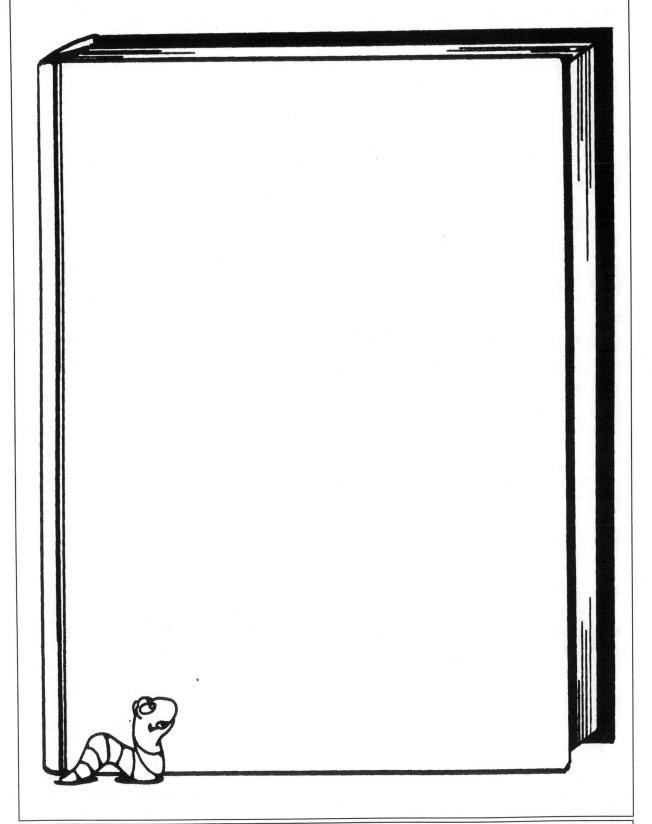

Fun Poetry

Poetry can be fun!

I am a little snail,

Who has a small grey tail.

My home I carry on my back.

And now I've found a leaf to snack.

Try your own poem.

_____

_____

_____

_____

_____

_____

_____

Non-fiction Quiz

1. What is non-fiction?_____

_____

2. How are non-fiction books arranged on the shelves?

_____

3. At what numbers would we find the following subjects:

Computers?_____   Poetry?_____

Animals?_____   Trees?_____

Cookery?_____   Cars?_____

Tennis?_____   Fables?_____

Prehistoric Animals?_____   Space Exploration?_____

4. **Locate one of the above subjects.**

Write down the:

* Author:_____

* Title:_____

* Call/Dewey number:_____

Reference Material

Have you used either of the following? (Tick the box.)

Encyclopaedias [ ]

Dictionaries [ ]

How are they similar?_____

_____

_____

Locate the reference shelves in your library. Look through the books on these shelves.

What do they include?

(a)_____

(b)_____

(c)_____

(d)_____

What are reference materials?_____

_____

_____

Encyclopaedias

What are encyclopaedias? _____

_____

_____

_____

How do we use encyclopaedias correctly? _____

_____

_____

_____

Name one set of encyclopaedias.

_____

Using Encyclopaedias

Pick an animal.

My animal is_____

Draw a picture of the animal.

Where does it live?_____

_____

What does it eat?_____

_____

How does it move around?_____

_____

What type of covering does your animal have?

For example, wool, feathers, skin, fur._____

Dictionaries

Dictionaries are lists of words and their meanings arranged in alphabetical order.

Write the dictionary meaning of these words:

Fruit_____

_____

Clown_____

_____

Book_____

_____

Car_____

_____

Light_____

_____

Reference Quiz

1. What are reference materials? _____

   _____

2. List two examples.

   (a)_____

   (b)_____

3. **Choose one of the above.**

   Explain how to use it._____

   _____

   _____

   _____

4. How are encyclopaedias and dictionaries similar?

   _____

   _____

Sleuth

R	E	F	E	Y	R	E	N	C	E	B	E	A
O	O	K	S	R	C	A	N	N	O	T	N	L
B	R	E	T	A	A	K	E	N	F	R	C	P
D	E	F	I	N	I	T	I	O	N	O	Y	H
E	F	M	T	O	H	E	L	I	B	R	C	A
L	E	A	R	I	F	A	B	L	E	S	L	B
A	R	Y	B	T	E	C	A	U	S	E	O	E
T	E	T	H	C	E	Y	A	R	E	T	P	T
K	N	H	E	I	R	E	F	O	R	A	A	I
L	C	N	Y	D	E	M	U	L	O	V	E	C
O	E	O	N	E	W	H	O	N	E	E	D	A
F	D	S	Y	R	T	E	O	P	I	N	I	L
F	O	R	M	A	T	I	O	N	T	C	A	F

Find the following words:

Alphabetical	Encyclopaedia	Poetry
Definition	Fables	Reference
Dictionary	Fact	Volume
	Folktale	

What message do the unused letters make? _____

_____

_____

Bingo

Requirements
One card per student
Counters
Word cards (for bingo caller)

What to do:
Students are given a card. The Bingo caller chooses a word and calls it out clearly. The first person to cover all the words on his or her card with the counters calls 'Bingo' and is the winner.

Cut out individual cards below.

Atlas	Index	Author
Library	Catalogue	Non-fiction
Dewey Decimal	Contents Page	Computers
Reference	Dictionary	Spine Label
Fiction	Title	Encyclopaedia